Cambridge Primary

Hodder Cambridge Primary
English
Workbook

Stage 2

Sarah Snashall

Series editor: Moira Brown

HODDER
EDUCATION
AN HACHETTE UK COMPANY

Stories about my world

Spelling ee and ea

1 Can you remember how to spell these words?
Write **ee** or **ea** in the gap to complete the word.

a sl _____ p

b f _____ t

c qu _____ n

d s _____

e Here is a cup of t _____ .

f Pl _____ se can I play?

g We have one sweet _____ ch.

h The grass was very gr _____ n.

2 Circle the words in this cloud that have a **long ee** sound:

neat   net   nest   leaves   red   easy   nice

letter   wheel   sneeze   bend

3 Add the words from activity 2 to this table.
Add two words of your own to each column.

	ee spelt ee	ee spelt ea
for example	seed need	eat treat
Add words from Activity 2		
My own words		

and but because

1 Use these words to fill in the gap in these sentences.

> and   but   because

a   My feet hurt _____ my shoes are too small.

b   I packed my bag _____ I put on my coat.

c   Eat your breakfast _____ brush your teeth.

d   Harriet dropped the cup _____ it didn't break.

e   The queen screamed _____ she saw a tiger.

f   Chico bumped his arm _____ he didn't cry.

2 Draw lines to match the sentence beginning with the right ending.

a   We cannot go to the park because   I am not wearing my boots.

b   We cannot go to the park but   it is raining.

c   I want to splash in puddles but   we can watch television.

When Dad Went Fishing

1 These pictures come from 'When Chico Went Fishing' by Robin Tzannes, illustrated by Korky Paul. Match the captions below to the pictures and use them to make up the story of Chico's Dad's fishing trip. Tell it to a partner.

a   He took out his tin of worms but unfortunately he dropped it and all the worms ran away.

b   He walked quickly but he slipped on a rock and fell in.

c   He hung up his clothes to dry and started fishing. He looked a bit silly because his fishing line was in a terrible muddle.

d   Chico's father picked up his fishing rod and headed to the river.

Character and setting

1 Are these pictures settings or characters?
Write 'setting' or 'character' under each one.

Fuego

Antonio

Treasure Island

_____

Bessie

Fab Fun Fair

Lucky

_____

2 Choose two characters and a setting from above and write an idea for a story. Use the table below to help you plan your story.

My story ideas:

Characters	
Setting	
Beginning	
Middle	
End	

Feelings

 Look at these scenes. Choose a word from the word bank to match how the character might be feeling.

a

_____

Word bank

frightened
happy
surprised
cross
pleased
shy
upset
brave

b

_____

c

_____

2 Complete a sentence for each picture. Use the word bank and these words to help you: **lost   wood   won   toy   treasure**

a Princess Shakura was _____ because _____

b Antonio was _____ because _____

c Pirate Bessie was _____ because _____

Past tense

1 All these sentences happened in the **past**. Choose the right word and write it in the space.

  a Princess Shakura _____ into the woods. (**ran   runs**)

  b Cinderella _____ at the ball. (**dances   danced**)

  c Bessie _____ the treasure chest. (**opened   opens**)

  d Antonio _____ to the top of the castle. (**climbed   climbs**)

  e The robot _____ the room. (**tidied   tidies**)

  f The shop _____ shut. (**is   was**)

2 Read this story beginning.

Jazmine was so excited. She was in the city with her sister Natasha and at any moment the circus was going to arrive. Holding hands tightly, they waited eagerly at the side of the road. Suddenly, Jazmine could see a flash of red in the distance and could just about hear the band playing. "Here they come!" she cried.

  a Circle the names of the two characters.

  b Underline the two words that tell us about the setting.

  c Is the story written in the **past tense** or the **present tense**?
   past tense ☐   present tense ☐

  d Write three past tense verbs from the passage.

  _____

  e Find three adverbs (–**ly** words) in the passage.

  _____

Captain Ace

1 Draw a character to go with this description.

Captain Ace was very tall and had big strong muscles. He had lovely curly brown hair and big brown eyes. When he smiled you could see his bright shiny white teeth. Captain Ace was a superhero so he dressed liked one! He wore red tights and a red top with a big A on it and a long blue cape.

2 Draw your own superhero.
Write some describing words about your superhero in the word bank.

Word bank

height _____

hair_____

eyes _____

mouth _____

clothes _____

Use the word bank to help you write two sentences about your superhero. Remember to use a capital letter and a full stop.

_____

_____

Self-assessment

Unit 1

Stories about my world

	😊 I understand this well
	😐 I understand this but need more practice
	🙁 I don't understand this

Learning Objective	😊	😐	🙁
Reading			
I can read aloud clearly, taking notice of the punctuation and speech marks.			
I can say who the characters are in a story.			
I can say where a story is set.			
I can work out how the characters in a story are feeling.			
I can talk about what happens at the beginning, middle and end of a story.			
Writing			
I can read and spell words with the **long ee** and **ai** phonemes.			
I can spell words ending in –**ly**.			
I can write a sentence with two ideas joined together with *and, but* and *because*.			
I can write a sentence with a capital letter and a full stop.			
I can write a sentence in the past tense.			
Speaking and listening			
I can act out part of a story.			

I need more help with ...

_____

_____

_____

_____

Unit 2 Instructions

Instructions

1 These instructions to make a fruit salad are in a muddle.
Write them in the correct order.

| Serve with ice-cream. | How to make a fruit salad | Cut up the fruit into bite-sized pieces. |

| You will need: three different types of fruit, orange juice, ice-cream | Add a cup of orange juice. |

_____

_____

_____

_____

2 Circle the signs that are instructions.

The ai phoneme

1 Write the words below in the correct spelling carriage.
One has been done for you.

drain	game	spray
display	complain	snake
clay	always	snail
amaze	plain	shake

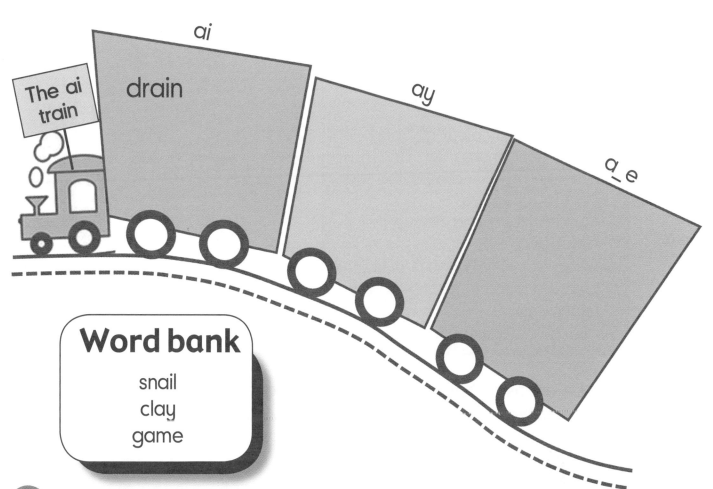

Word bank

snail
clay
game

2 Use the word bank above to complete the sentences
using an **ai** word.

a The boy enjoyed the _____.

b The _____ moved very slowly.

c The pot is made from _____.

11

Instruction features

 Draw a line from the labels below to the features in this instruction text.

(Title)   ('What you need' list)   (Numbered points)

(Illustrations)   (Command words)

How to make a fishtail loom band bracelet

You will need:
loom bands in three colours, loom band catch

1 Put the first colour of band over two fingers in a figure of eight.
2 Put the second colour of band over the top of the first but without a twist.
3 Put the third colour of band over your fingers.
4 Pull the first band over the top of the other two.
5 Add a new band above the other two.
6 Repeat points 4 and 5 until you have a band long enough for your wrist.
7 Fasten with a catch.

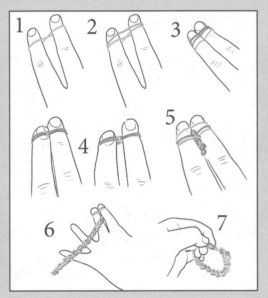

2 Write an instruction to go with these signs. Remember to use command verbs.

a _____   b _____   c _____

_____   _____   _____

_____   _____   _____

How to make a butterfly with spots

 Complete these instructions for making a model of a butterfly.

How to make a spotty butterfly

You will need:

coloured _____   _____

antennae made of wire   _____

_____   _____

_____   _____

What to do:

1 Fold a piece of coloured card in half.

2 _____
_____
_____

3 _____
_____
_____

4 Colour in the body with a black felt tip pen.

5 Stick coloured spots _____
_____
_____

6 Use sticky tape to _____
_____
the antennae.

Instruction words

 There are some words missing in this recipe for making pancakes. Write the missing words in the clues below and then complete the crossword. You can choose from these words:

> quickly finally next first carefully careful gently slowly

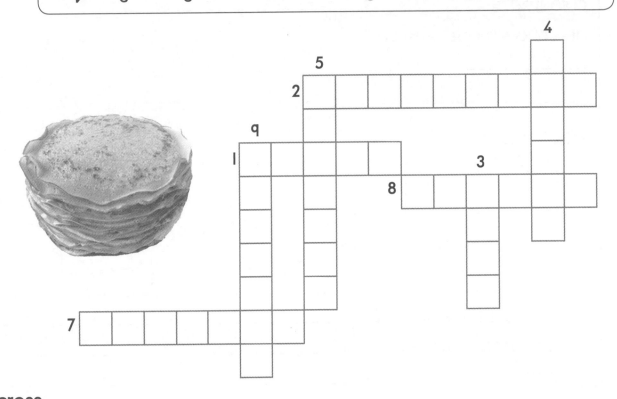

Across

1 _____ put the flour in a bowl.

2 Crack the egg _____ into a cup.

7 _____ pour a little mixture into the frying pan.

8 After a few minutes, _____ turn the pancake over.

Down

3 _____ add the egg to the flour.

4 Stir in the milk _____.

5 Heat some oil in a pan. _____ it will be hot!

9 _____ serve the pancake with lemon and sugar.

Castle walk

1 Look at this map and draw the route with a coloured pencil.
To get from the bakery to the castle:

1 Come out of the bakery and turn left.

2 Go over the bridge.

3 Turn right and go around the bend.

4 You have arrived at the castle.

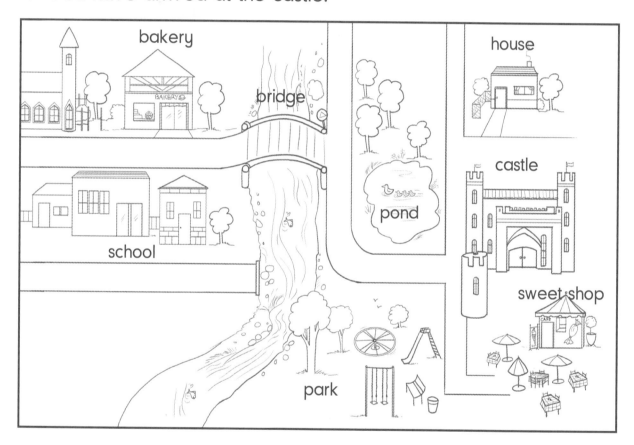

2 Look at the map again and draw this route:

a Start at the sweet shop.

b Walk straight on and then turn right.

c Turn left opposite the castle.

d Go straight past the pond and around the bend.

e Go left over the bridge.

What building is on your left? _____

Who, why and when

1 Find these words in the word search.

who what why when where how which

h	o	w	o	w	l
h	i	h	b	h	w
r	e	e	p	y	h
l	c	n	c	h	o
a	w	h	e	r	e
g	r	u	o	w	o
w	h	i	c	h	g
w	l	w	h	a	t

2 Write your own question sentences.
Remember to end each with a question mark.

1 Who put _____

2 Where are _____

3 How did _____

4 Why is _____

Self-assessment

Unit 2
Instructions

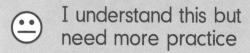

☺ I understand this well

😐 I understand this but need more practice

☹ I don't understand this

Learning Objective	☺	😐	☹
Reading			
I can read the question words: *what, where, when, who, why* and answer questions that use them.			
I can read and follow an instruction text.			
I can talk about the features of an instruction text.			
Writing			
I know the main spellings for the **long ai** and **ee** phonemes.			
I can create an adverb using **–ly**.			
I can write instructions using command words.			
I can use words that show time in my writing: *first, after that, next.*			
Speaking and listening			
I can give my classmates clear instructions, speaking so they can understand me.			

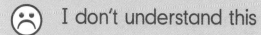

I need more help with ...

_____

_____

_____

_____

Unit 3 Poems about me

Rhyming words

1 Draw a line between the words that rhyme.
The first one has been done for you.

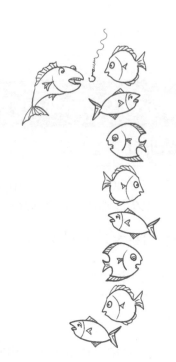

silly —————————	chilly
light	motion
potion	crowned
stone	kite
ground	flown

2 The rhyming words in this poem are at the end of the line.
Circle each rhyming pair of words in a different colour.
You will need four different colours.

One, two, three, four, five

Once I caught a fish alive.

Six, seven, eight, nine, ten.

Then I let it go again.

Why did you let it go?

Because it bit my finger so!

Which finger did it bite?

This little finger on the right.

Hidden picture

 Colour in the words shown in the key to reveal a picture!

Key
- Colour words with the **long oa** phoneme yellow (as in b**oa**t, st**o**n**e** and sn**ow**)
- Colour words with the **long igh** phoneme red (as in sl**i**d**e**, l**igh**t, cr**y** and p**ie**)
- Colour words with the **long ai** phoneme blue (as in r**ai**n, pl**ay** and pl**a**t**e**)
- Colour words with the **long ow** phoneme green (as in cl**ou**d and cl**ow**n)

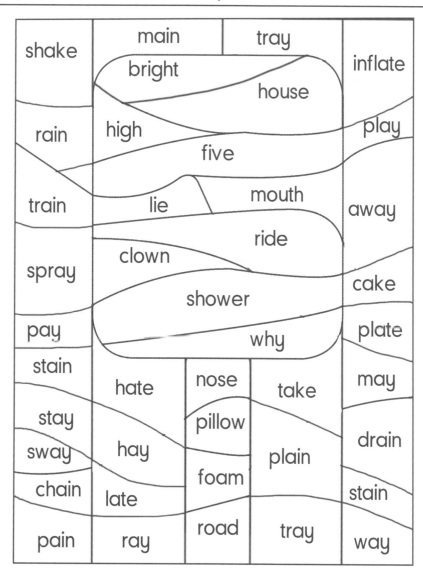

Performing a poem

1 Practise for a performance of this poem.
Make notes on the poem about how you are going to read it.

- Write: **Quiet, Getting louder, Loud, Getting quieter, Quiet**
  next to the verses to show how you are going to read them.
- Circle all the lines that end with an exclamation mark.
  You will want to say these lines louder.
- Draw a circle around the words that rhyme in each verse.

Monsters!

Big heads	And moles
Big feet	And warts
Big hands	And stinks
Big seat	And snorts
Monsters!	Monsters!
Sharp teeth	Some mean
Sharp nails	Some mad
Sharp ears	Some kind
Sharp tails	Some sad
Monsters!	Monsters!
With scales	
With wings	*By Philip Waddell*
With horns	
With stings	
Monsters!	

Syllables

1 How many syllables are there in these words?
Clap the syllables in each word then circle the right answer.

again	1	2	3		through	1	2	3
which	1	2	3		animal	1	2	3
carefully	1	2	3		another	1	2	3
dragon	1	2	3		was	1	2	3
river	1	2	3					

2 Move through the table to find out which shield belongs to
Captain Ace. Start at the start sign. Say each word, clap the
syllables and use the key to follow the route to the shield:

↑   one syllable word: go up

↓   two syllable word: go down

→   three syllable word: go right

again	animal	another	dragon	which	B
was	another	carefully	again	was	E
carefully	through	again	dragon	which	D
another	was	river	animal	river	C
animal →	which	was	which	another	A
START ↑	through	carefully	another	river	F

Choosing a cake

 Finish this poem using adjectives of your choice or choose adjectives from the box. They can go in any order you like – whatever you think sounds good.

> big, little, sticky, gooey, fairy, carrot, ginger, lemon, chocolate, birthday, wedding, swirly, twirly, pink, green, cream, stripy, spotty

_____ cakes, _____ cakes,

_____ and _____ and _____ cakes.

_____ cakes, _____ cakes.

What a lovely smell!

_____ cakes, _____ cakes

_____, _____, _____ cakes.

I wish I'd eaten fewer cakes.

I don't feel very well!

Self-assessment

Unit 3
Poems about me

	:) I understand this well
:)-	I understand this but need more practice
:(	I don't understand this

Learning Objective	:)	:|	:(
Reading			
I can count the syllables in a word.			
I can spot words that rhyme.			
I can read poems with expression.			
I can clap the rhythm in a poem.			
I can find the adjectives in a poem.			
Writing			
I know different spellings for the following phonemes:			
long *ai*			
long *oa*			
long *ow*			
long *igh*			
I can use the past tense.			
I can write a poem based on a poem I've read.			
Speaking and listening			
I can make what I'm saying interesting to listen to.			

I need more help with ...

_____

_____

_____

_____

Tales from around the world

The fool and the rich man

 Circle the words with the **long oo** phoneme in this story.
Can you find 15 different words?

> **Hint**: look for words spelled *oo, u_e, ew, ue*.
> There are also four words with the *oo* phoneme that
> are spelled differently – but you know these very well.

The fool and the rich man

One day, the fool Nasriddin was invited to a rich man's house for
dinner. When he arrived, the house was filled with the perfume of a
delicious stew. But when he sat down the rich man began to tell
stories about himself. The fool grew hungry but didn't want to be rude
so he listened politely. After two hours, the night had turned cool and
the moon and stars could be seen, but the rich man was still talking.
Who would rescue him?

In the end, the fool knew he had
to do something otherwise he
would go hungry. He said to the
rich man, "In these stories, did you
ever eat?" The rich man took the
hint and asked that the food
be served.

And it was worth the wait.

By Sarah Snashall

Story settings

 1 Choose one of the settings from the box to match to each story opening.

> A hut in the mountains.
> An old castle.
> The seaside.
> A city in the future.
> A school.
> Underwater.

I Matchet put on his seat belt and flew his robot car into the air joining the traffic above New City 2.

_____

_____

2 Ollie Octopus looked out of his cave. The fish and crabs wanted to talk to him but he felt too shy to talk to them.

_____

_____

3 Andrew looked out of the window of the hut and could see nothing but the valley and the mountains. This was going to be the world's worst holiday.

_____

4 Malia sat at her desk. All her friends were chatting but she needed to finish her homework. If not, she knew she would be in trouble as soon as the teacher arrived.

_____

5 Zach climbed the stone tower holding the candle so tightly that it shook in his hand. Where was the noise he had heard coming from?

_____

6 Finn felt the tide lap over his feet and then wash back again. He pressed his feet further into the wet sand.

_____

Who's talking?

 1 Circle the name of the person who is talking in each sentence and underline what they are saying.

a The Emperor looked at his advisors sternly and said in a low tone, "Someone pulled my hair."

b "Lock him up!" shouted the advisors to the Emperor.

c "He should be given sweets," said Birbal gently to the Emperor.

d Staring at Birbal open mouthed the advisors cried, "He is crazy!"

2 Complete these sentences by finishing what the characters could say.

a Running up to his friend's house, Olaf shouted, "Anders, would you

_____

b "One, two, three," counted Anita while her friends hid. "_____

_____

c " _____ "

whispered Disha to Anita as they walked to school.

d "Once you have cleaned your teeth," said Mum, "Please would

you _____

A box of sweets

1 Read 'A box of sweets' on Learner's Book page 58.
Write 'true' or 'false' next to these statements about the story.

a The Emperor is really cross about having his hair pulled.

_____

b The Emperor has four foolish advisors.

_____

c When we read the story, we know that the Emperor is playing
a trick. _____

d The Emperor knows that Birbal will not fall for the trick.

_____

e Birbal says that the Emperor should be given a box of sweets.

_____

How the elephant got his trunk

1 Read this story opening and complete the answers to the questions.

How the elephant got his trunk

In the first days, the elephant had a stubby little nose like a hippo, but he didn't mind because he didn't know any better. At that time there was a new elephant – an elephant's child – and he asked ever so many questions. One day he asked, "What does a crocodile have for dinner?" His parents wouldn't tell him and his aunts and uncles wouldn't tell him so he went to find out for himself. When he found the crocodile lying in the river he asked, "Excuse me, Mr Crocodile, what do you have for dinner?"

"Well, today," replied the crocodile, "I'm going to have elephant's child."

by Rudyard Kipling
adapted by Sarah Snashall

1 What is this story about?

The story is about how _____.

2 When is the story set? Now or a long time ago?

The story is set _____.

I know this because it says _____.

3 Who are the two main characters?

_____.

4 How is the elephant's child going to get a trunk?

I think the elephant's child will get a trunk when _____

_____.

Compound words

1 How many compound words can you find in this table?
Join two words together and write them on the lines below.
You can use words more than once. See the example below.

trouble	any	where	hair	some
some	pot	every	brush	barrow
wheel	tea	one	time	how

troublesome, _____

_____

_____

_____

2 Choose four of the compound words that you found in activity 1
and use them to write a sentence. Use an adjective in each
sentence. Choose one from this box.

> red, favourite, tall, bendy, colourful, soft, useful,
> poisonous, tired, tangled, broken, lovely

For example: I have lost my favourite hairbrush.

a _____

_____

b _____

_____

c _____

_____

d _____

_____

Beginning, middle and end

1 **The Emperor's Lost Ring**

Put these events into the right order to make a story.

a One night, while the Emperor was sleeping a thief stole a ruby ring from his finger.

b "There's your thief!" cried Birbal. The advisor was searched and the ring was found in his pocket.

c "A thief is always waiting to be caught," explained Birbal.

d "Do not worry, your Majesty," said Birbal. "The thief is in this room and he has straw in his beard."

e One of Akbar's advisors put his hand up to his beard.

f "Thank you, Birbal," smiled the Emperor. "That was a clever trick."

g Once upon a time there was a mighty ruler called Emperor Akbar who had a clever advisor called Birbal.

h The Emperor was very upset because the ring was precious.

The order of the story should be: _____

2 Complete these sentences.

At the beginning of the story: _____

_____

In the middle of the story: _____

_____

At the end of the story: _____

_____

Self-assessment

Unit 4

Tales from around the world

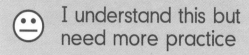 I understand this well

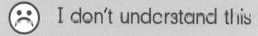 I understand this but need more practice

☹ I don't understand this

Learning Objective	☺	😐	☹
Reading			
I can read words with a **long *oo*** phoneme.			
I can split a compound word into two parts.			
I can count the syllables in a word.			
I can show where the speech marks are in a story.			
I can say what the setting is in a story.			
I can suggest what the characters might be thinking.			
I can talk about the adjectives that describe the setting and characters.			
Writing			
I can use what I've learned about phonemes and spelling patterns to try and spell words correctly.			
I can write a story with a beginning, middle and end.			
Speaking and listening			
I can explain my story plan and ideas.			
I can listen carefully to a partner's ideas and ask questions.			

I need more help with ...

_____

_____

_____

_____

 Amazing plants

Different books

1 Draw a line to match each book to its purpose.

to explain

to give instructions

to give information

to entertain

2 Complete these sentences about the different types of non-fiction text.

a An explanation text tells us _____.

b An information text tells us _____.

c An instruction text tells us _____.

Oh or Ow!

 Help Diya to follow the words with the **oa** phoneme to get to the party. The first step has been done for you. Remember, the **oa** phoneme can be spelled: **oa** as in boat, **ow** as in blown or **o_e** as in over.

Tip! Watch out for words that say 'ow' (as in cow) – they will take you the wrong way!

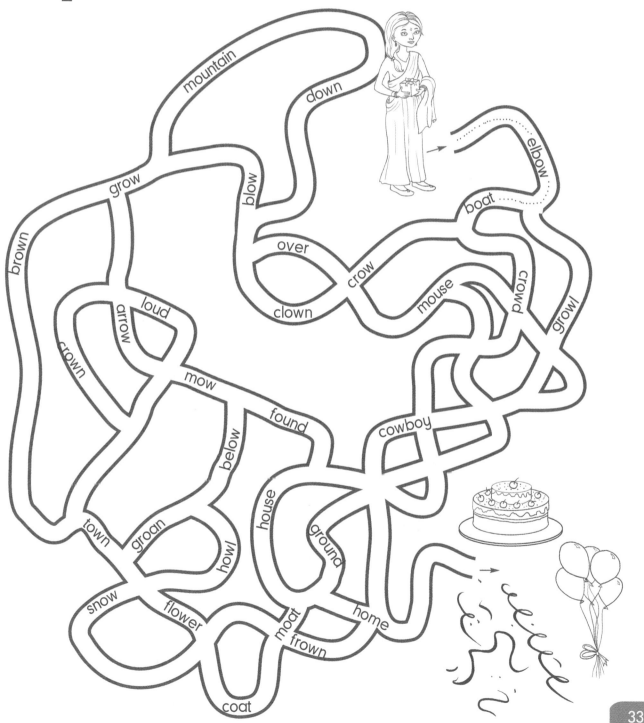

How a broad bean grows

 1 Look at this explanation text about how broad beans grow.
Draw a line from the labels below to the correct part of the text.

(label) (introduction) (diagram) (caption) (heading)

How a broad bean grows

Broad beans grow from a seed and are very easy to grow.

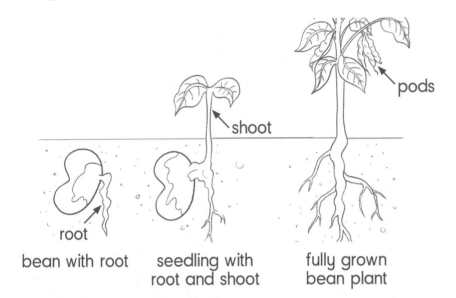

bean with root   seedling with root and shoot   fully grown bean plant

1 First the bean grows a root. Then it grows a shoot.
2 The shoot turns into a seedling.
3 When the plant is fully grown, flowers grow on the bean plant.
4 After the flowers die, they turn into bean pods with new beans inside.
5 When the beans have dried they become bean seeds.

2 Answer these questions.

a What happens to the shoot? _____

b What is a seedling? _____

c When does the bean plant grow bean pods? _____

_____

d Where do the beans grow? _____

Why flowers need bees

1 Read the information text about 'Why flowers need bees'.

Why flowers need bees

Plants need the help of bees to make fruit or seeds. They produce flowers to attract the bees. Flowers contain sweet liquid called nectar that bees just love to drink! When a bee lands on a flower to drink the nectar, a yellow dust called pollen sticks to its body. When the bee lands on the next plant, the pollen on its body and the flower mix together. This is called pollination.
After pollination, the flower is able to turn into a fruit or a seed.

2 Answer these questions.

a Why do plants need bees? _____

_____

b How does the pollen move from plant to plant? _____

_____

c Where do bees find nectar? _____

_____

3 Match the definitions to the words.

a sweet liquid found in flowers

pollen

when pollen from one flower
is taken to another flower

nectar

pollination   a yellow powder on flowers

Toil with the oi phoneme

1 Complete the words in these sentences using *oi* or *oy*.

a The b____ planted a sunflower seed in the s____l.

b The opera singer made a terrible n____se with

his v____ce!

c Harry had a difficult ch____ce. Which club should he

j____n?

d "Enj____ the v____age" said the captain of the ship.

e Rianna had two pound c____ns in her purse, enough

to buy the t____.

2 Find these words with the *oi* phoneme.

annoy

boil

foil

joint

joy

oil

oyster

royal

spoil

toil

j	o	y	r	p	i
o	i	s	o	b	n
i	l	p	y	o	g
n	w	o	a	i	f
t	o	i	l	l	o
r	b	l	v	r	i
a	n	n	o	y	l
o	y	s	t	e	r

Present tense practice

1 Put a tick next to the sentences that are written in the present tense. Draw a circle around the verb that tells you it is in the present tense.

a The bee lands on the flower. ☐

b The pollen drops off the bee. ☐

c The boy planted the seeds. ☐

d I bought a new toy. ☐

e We watched the bean plant grow and grow. ☐

f We swim in the sea on holiday. ☐

2 Write a present tense sentence to go with each of these pictures. Remember to use a capital letter and a full stop.

> **Hint:** Write the sentence as if it is happening right now.

park

boy

cake

children

_____

_____

_____

_____

_____

_____

Mm crossword

1 Use the text on Learner's Book page **82** to help you to find the answers to these crossword clues.

Across

1 A very small furry animal with a long tail and a pointed nose.

2 The time between dawn and midday.

3 A very high hill.

Down

4 A bicycle with an engine.

5 It goes round the earth every twenty eight days.

6 A type of wide, fast road.

2 Look up these words in a dictionary, then join the word to its definition.

lace	from a different country
lead	a material with a pattern of small holes in it
iguana	a large lizard that lives in trees in hot countries
igloo	a soft, grey metal that is very heavy
foreign	a house made from blocks of hard snow or ice
forehead	the part of your face above your eyes

Self-assessment

Unit 5

Amazing plants

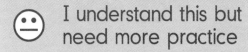 ☺	I understand this well
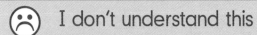 😐	I understand this but need more practice
☹	I don't understand this

Learning Objective	☺	😐	☹
Reading			
I can find out the meaning of a new word using a dictionary.			
I can point out the features of an explanation text.			
I can find the key (important) words in an explanation text.			
Writing			
I know different spellings for the phonemes:			
ee			
ou			
oa			
oi			
I can put words of the same letter into alphabetical order.			
I can point out verbs in the present tense.			
I can point out verbs in the past tense.			
I can write a sentence in the present tense.			
I can make notes by writing down key words.			
I can use a connective (*and, but, because*) to join two sentences together.			
Speaking and listening			
I can explain an idea clearly using key words.			

I need more help with ...

_____

_____

_____

Favourite poets

Rhyming words

1 Look at the words in the bubble. Circle words that rhyme in the same colour. You will need four different colours.

drowned

peel   tower   book

feet   crawl   new

cream   ground   beat

ball   pour   horse

clue   room   loud

2 Choose different spellings for the *or* phoneme to complete these sentences.

a   Ramah arrived with a present f____ her grandmother.

b   I have f____ brothers – Jude, Samuel, Joseph and Saul.

c   The kitten scratched the chair with her cl____s.

d   "Be careful you don't trip and f____ll!" called the teacher.

Adjectives

1 Add an adjective from the box to each word in this scene.

boat

beachball

waves

girls

crab

feet

pearl

lunch

crashing
sandy
scuttling
tasty
speedy
bouncy
shiny
playing

2 Use the adjectives above – or your own – to complete this list poem about the seaside.

Five things you find at the seaside

_____ girls

_____ pearls

_____ feet

_____ lunch to eat

_____ waves

Happy days!

3 Find a word with the **ur** phoneme on this page and write it in the chart. Then add another word to each column.

ur	ir	ear

The End

The End

When I was One
I had just begun.

When I was Two,
I was nearly new.

When I was Three,
I was hardly Me.

When I was Four,
I was not much more.

When I was Five,
I was just alive.

But now I am Six, I'm as clever as clever.
So I think I'll be six now forever and ever.

A A Milne

Rhyming crossword

 1 Answer these questions about 'The End' by A A Milne on page 42 and use your answers to fill in the crossword.

Across

2 What word rhymes with 'Two'? _____

4 What word rhymes with 'Four'? _____

5 What word rhymes with 'Five'? _____

Down

I What word rhymes with 'One'? _____

3 What word rhymes with 'Three'? _____

6 What word rhymes with 'clever'? _____

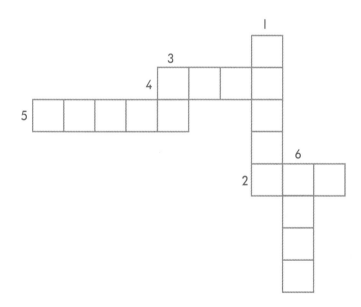

2 Match the phoneme to the word by drawing a line.

two   **long *ee*** phoneme

one   **short *e*** phoneme

me   ***w*** phoneme

ever   **long *oo*** phoneme

Rhyming race

 Play this game with a friend.

How to play:

1 Place a counter for each player on the start square.

2 Each player rolls a dice and moves the correct number of squares.

3 When players land on a square with a task, they complete it.
If they complete the task correctly, they stay on the square.
If they don't, they go back three squares.

4 The winner is the first player to reach the end.

Start

1	2	3 Read the word: **never** Close your eyes and spell it.	4	5	6 Which of these words rhymes with bed? head bead feed
12 Which of these words rhymes with curl? kerb car girl	11	10	9 Read the word: **really** Close your eyes and spell it.	8	7
13	14	15 Read the word: **every** Close your eyes and spell it.	16	17	18 Which of these words rhymes with hive? give five high
24 Which of these words rhymes with for? pour form from	23	22	21 Read the word: **first** Close your eyes and spell it.	20	19
25	26	27 Read the word: **earth** Close your eyes and spell it.	28	29	30 Which of these words rhymes with broom? brown brick bloom

Finish

Self-assessment

Unit 6

Favourite poets

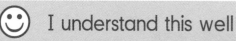 I understand this well

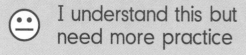 I understand this but need more practice

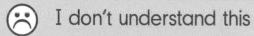 I don't understand this

Learning Objective	🙂	😐	🙁
Reading			
I can find the words that rhyme in a poem.			
I can clap the beat in a poem.			
I can answer questions about a poem.			
I can talk about the words in a poem.			
I can talk about the rhyme and rhythm in a poem.			
Writing			
I know different spellings for the following phonemes:			
long *or*			
long *ee*			
long *oo*			
long *ou*			
long *ur*			
I remember to check my work after completing an activity.			
I can write a list poem.			
I can add an adjective to a noun to make my writing more interesting.			
Speaking and listening			
I can perform a poem using expression to make it sound interesting.			

I need more help with ...

_____

_____

_____

_____

Unit 7 The wonderful Roald Dahl

Juicy crossword

1 These adjectives come from 'The Enormous Crocodile'. Match the adjective to the clue to complete the crossword.

> enormous, muddiest, nasty, bitter, chewy, tough, juicy

Across

1 Full of juice

3 Very large

6 The opposite of sweet

7 Another word for horrible

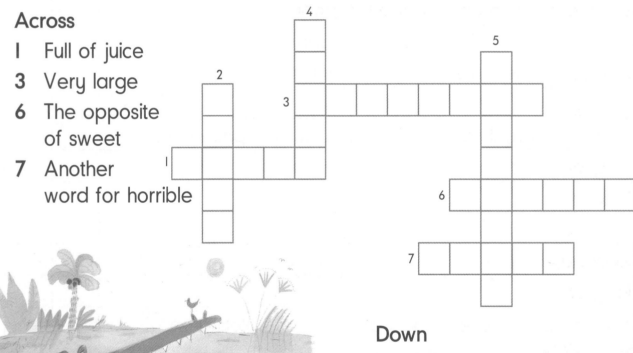

Down

2 Hard to eat

4 Needs to be chewed many times.

5 The most muddy

2 Complete these sentences using some adjectives of your own.

a The chewy sweet tasted _____ and _____.

b I was walking down the road when I saw an enormous _____

_____cat. It was_____.

Long vowel practice

 The **long ar** phoneme is normally spelt **ar** as in dark.
Write a word with the **ar** phoneme for each picture below.

a

_____

b

_____

c

_____

d

_____

2 All of these words contain a long vowel phoneme **ee, ar, igh** or **ai**.
Write **ee, ar, igh** or **ai** next to each word to show which long vowel
phoneme is used.

> **Tip:** Look at Learner's Book page 102 for the
> different spelling of each long vowel phoneme.

park   _____   price   _____

dark   _____   gave   _____

hard   _____   rain   _____

harp   _____   meat   _____

my   _____   sheet   _____

dis, un, –.ly, ful

1 Dis–. or un–.? Choose the right word for each sentence.

a Can you help me _____ the shopping?

| dispack unpack |

b Please _____ your laces before you take your shoes off.

| disdo undo |

c Good children will never _____ their teacher.

| disobey unobey |

d Don't _____ when it is time to do the washing up.

| disappear unappear |

2 add –.ly to these words to make adverbs.

a final _____

b sudden _____

c cheery _____

d brave _____

e sweet _____

3 Write four sentences each using a different adverb from activity 2. Remember to use a capital letter and a full stop.

a _____

b _____

c _____

d _____

An unlucky word search

1 Find and circle the words in the box below which use the prefixes
un– and **dis–** or the suffixes **–ly** and **–ful** in the word search.

w	o	n	u	n	w	e	l	l	b
a	p	u	n	h	a	p	p	y	z
s	t	r	t	s	l	o	w	l	y
h	c	d	i	s	a	g	r	e	e
a	a	c	d	i	s	l	i	k	e
p	r	e	y	f	j	y	n	y	q
p	e	s	h	e	l	p	f	u	l
i	f	p	a	i	n	f	u	l	u
l	u	c	k	i	l	y	i	o	n
y	l	t	x	b	t	e	v	a	p

untidy

unhappy

unwell

luckily

happily

slowly

careful

painful

helpful

dislike

disagree

2 Choose a word from the box above to complete the sentence.
Use a word starting or ending with a prefix or suffix.

a I have eaten four mangoes and now I feel _____.

b _____, the door creaked open.

c I _____ tidying my room but Mum says I have to.

d Can you be _____ and go to the shops?

Beginning, middle and end

1 Every story needs a beginning, a middle and an end.
Add the missing section to these story plans – use your own ideas based on the rest of the story.

1 **Beginning:** Once upon a time a caterpillar hatched out of an egg.

   Middle: The caterpillar ate and ate and went to sleep in a cocoon.

   End: _____

   _____

   _____

2 **Beginning:** There once was an Enormous Crocodile who wanted to eat children.

   Middle: _____

   _____

   End: Luckily, Humpy-Rumpy saw the trick and ran to rescue the children.

3 **Beginning:** Rafi was sad. He was lonely because he had no friends.

   Middle: One day, a new boy called Benji arrived at the school and Mrs Gosh asked Rafi to look after him.

   End: _____

   _____

   _____

Get talking

1 Fill in the empty speech bubbles with a reply.

2 Choose words from the box to complete this story.

> suddenly, one day, next, first

_____, Toto and Mary were picking coconuts in

the forest. _____, they picked up some coconuts

from the ground. _____, they chose a tree to climb.

_____, Humpy-Rumpy ran into the clearing.

"Look out!" he cried.

Question or not?

1 Add a full stop (.), question mark (?) or an exclamation mark (!) to the end of these sentences.

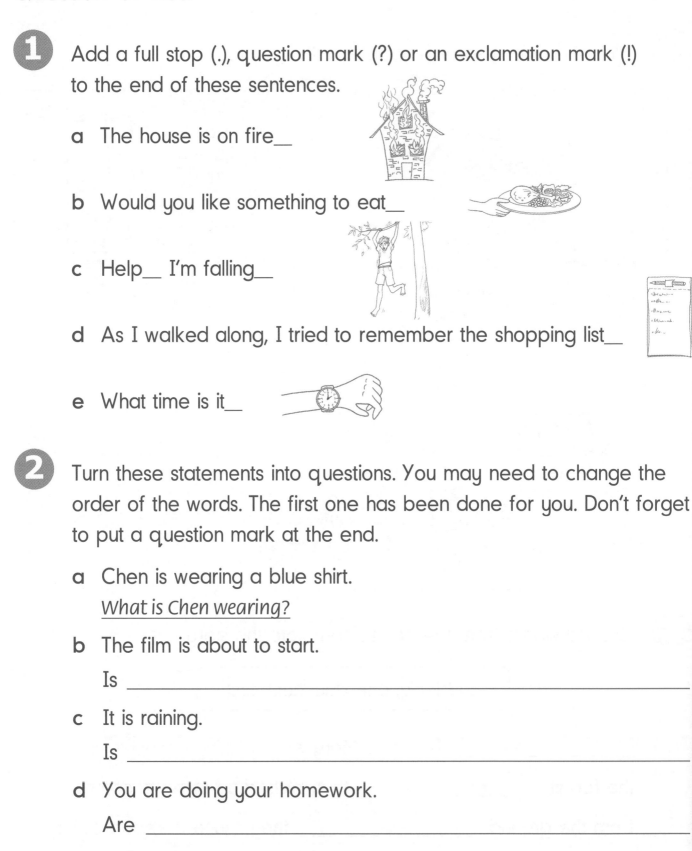

a The house is on fire__

b Would you like something to eat__

c Help__ I'm falling__

d As I walked along, I tried to remember the shopping list__

e What time is it__

2 Turn these statements into questions. You may need to change the order of the words. The first one has been done for you. Don't forget to put a question mark at the end.

a Chen is wearing a blue shirt.

 What is Chen wearing?

b The film is about to start.

 Is _____

c It is raining.

 Is _____

d You are doing your homework.

 Are _____

e You like to eat an ice-cream.

 Do _____

Self-assessment

Unit 7

The wonderful Roald Dahl

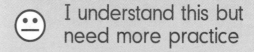 I understand this well

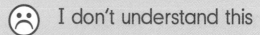 I understand this but need more practice

😞 I don't understand this

Learning Objective	😊	😐	😞
Reading			
I can read words with a **long *ar*** phoneme.			
I can read words with a **long *ai*** phoneme.			
I can read words with a **long *igh*** phoneme.			
I can read aloud clearly, taking notice of question and exclamation marks.			
I can show when somebody is speaking in a story.			
Writing			
I can change the meaning of a word using the prefix **un–**.			
I can change the meaning of a word using the prefix **dis–**.			
I can create an adjective by using the suffix **–ful**.			
I can create an adverb using the suffix **–ly**.			
I can plan a story with a *beginning*, a *middle* and an *end*.			
I can use adjectives and adverbs to describe the character and setting in my story.			
I can write different types of sentences using the words *and, but* and *because* to connect my ideas.			
I can start some sentences with words that show time such as *suddenly, after that, first*.			
Speaking and listening			
I can role play events from a story.			

I need more help with ...

_____

_____

_____

_____

53

Unit 8 Highest, longest, smallest

Smallest or tallest

1 Write sentences about these children.

Li Jun 1.05 m   Li Min 1.20 m   Wang Yong 1.50 m

1   Write a sentence that uses the word *tallest*.

_____

2   Write a sentence that uses the word *smallest*.

_____

3   Write a sentence that uses the word *taller*.

_____

4   Write a sentence that uses the word *smaller*.

_____

Ben's favourites

 1 Look at this chart and answer the questions.

	Favourite food	Least favourite food	Favourite sport	Favourite game
Ben	pizza	sushi	football	computer games
Lily	sushi	rice	tennis	computer games
Hope	sushi	pizza	tennis	chess

a Who likes computer games but does not like sushi?

_____

b Who loves sushi, tennis and computer games?

_____

c Who does not like rice but does like computer games?

_____

d How many children like sushi and computer games?

_____

2 Fill in the chart using these statements.

Cheng: I like curry but I do not like fish. I like to do karate.
My favourite superhero is Iron Man.
Fu: I like to pretend to be Batman when I practise karate.
My favourite food is stir-fry. My least favourite is bananas.
Hue: My three favourite things are: karate, ice-cream and Batman.
My least favourite thing is broccoli.

	Favourite food	Least favourite food	Favourite sport	Favourite superhero
Cheng				
Fu				
Hui				

Dictionary time

1 Put these words into alphabetical order.

before _____
there _____
friends _____
live _____
boat _____
cried _____

2 Find these words in a dictionary then match them to their definitions. Draw a line from the word to its definition.

floodlight   a building material made from a mixture of broken stone or gravel, sand, cement, and water

steel   a very tall building of many storeys

     a strong metal made of iron

concrete

     a large, powerful light, typically one of several used to illuminate a sports ground, skyscrapers   a stage, or the exterior of a building

un–, dis–, –ly, –ful

1 Circle the root word in these words. Remember: the root word is the word that has had **un–**, **dis–**, **–ly**, or **–ful** added to it.

unfit
displease
friendly
wonderful

2 Add **un–**, **dis–**, **–ly**, or **–ful** to these words. Use each prefix or suffix once. Remember, if a word ends in **y**, you must turn the **y** into **i** before adding **–ly**.

greedy _____

able _____

hope _____

load _____

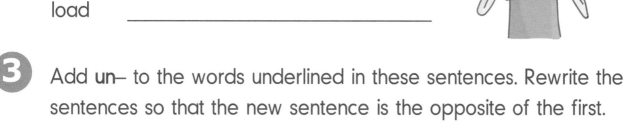

3 Add **un–** to the words underlined in these sentences. Rewrite the sentences so that the new sentence is the opposite of the first. You will need to change other words in the sentence.

a The <u>wise</u> advisor was very clever.

_____

b The boy came first in the race because he was very <u>fit</u>.

_____

c I am very <u>happy</u> because we are going to the seaside.

_____

The blue whale

The blue whale

The blue whale is the biggest animal that has ever lived. Adult blue whales weigh about 180 tons. Their tongue weighs as much as an elephant. Blue whales can grow up to 33 metres in length which is as long as three buses.

The blue whale comes to the surface to breathe.

Ocean homes

Blue whales live in all the Earth's oceans. They spend the winters in the north and move to the warm waters at the equator during summer.

The biggest land animal was the Argentinosaurus dinosaur. It was only half as big as a blue whale.

Small food

The blue whale eats only the smallest creatures. It catches krill using a trap in its mouth which is like a huge comb.

In danger

Sadly, in the past, people have hunted the big blue whale. Now they are in danger from pollution and from ships running into them. There are only about 4500 blue whales left.

Big blue whale

1 Fill in this chart about the big blue whale.

Whale facts	
Longest length	
Heaviest weight	
In danger from	
Number left	

2 Answer these questions about the report.

a The big blue whale is the biggest animal that has ever lived. true/false

b You are very likely to see a blue whale if you go out into the ocean. true/false

c The report on page 58 has a chart. true/false

d The report on page 58 has captions. true/false

3 Find these key words in the report.

> krill, largest, pollution

Write a sentence using each key word.

a _____

b _____

c _____

Amazon report

 1 Use words from the box to complete this Amazon report.

a Add a title here

_____

The Amazon is the second longest river in the world.

b Add a section title here

_____

The Amazon is about **6400** metres long. It travels from Peru to Brazil.

c Join a sentence

The Amazon is very wide _____ there is only one bridge over it.

d Add an extra fact here

_____

_____

e Add a caption here

_____

_____

_____

f Add two facts about Amazon animals here

Amazon animals

_____

_____

_____

There are over **3000** types of fish in the Amazon.	Turtles, bull sharks, caiman and snakes also live in the river.
The Amazon goes through the Amazon Rainforest.	Amazing Amazon
	but
A long and wide river	

You must read this

1 Use this writing frame to write a review of a book you would like to recommend to your friends.

Title: (The name of the book.)	
Author: (The person who wrote the book.)	
Illustrator: (The person who drew the pictures. Note: not all books have pictures. Sometimes the pictures are drawn by the author.)	
About the book: (Write two sentences about what happens in the book. Don't say what happens in the end. Use the language of time, for example, *at first, next, suddenly* and so on.)	
Why I like this book: (Write a sentence about what you like about the book. Use adjectives, for example, *funny, surprising, exciting.*)	
My favourite part: (Write a sentence about your favourite part of the book.)	

Quickly or slowly

1 Add –ly to the words given in brackets to complete these sentences.

Remember: if a word ends in y then turn the y into an i before you add –ly.

a _____ the boy cut out the picture. (careful)

b _____ the dragon looked at the gold. (greedy)

c _____ the plate did not break. (lucky)

d Alvaro read the book _____. (quiet)

e _____ Sebastian began to sing. (brave)

f The star shone _____ (bright)

2 Read this book report and then answer the questions.

Title: The Twits

Author: Roald Dahl

Illustrator: Quentin Blake

About the book: Mr and Mrs Twit are nasty and dirty people who play horrible tricks on each other. One day their pet monkeys play a trick on them.

Why I like this book: I like this book because it is full of funny tricks and because it has a happy ending. My favourite part is when Mrs Twit puts worms in Mr Twit's spaghetti.

a Who drew the pictures? _____

b Find two adjectives for Mr and Mrs Twit. _____

_____

c Do you think that Mr and Mrs Twit are kind to their pet monkeys?

_____ Why do you think that? _____

_____

Self-assessment

Unit 8

Highest, longest, smallest

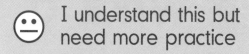 😊 I understand this well

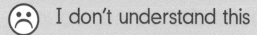 😐 I understand this but need more practice

😞 I don't understand this

Learning Objective	😊	😐	😞
Reading			
I can find answers by reading a table.			
I can spot headings, captions, diagrams and tables in a report text.			
Writing			
I can spell words with the suffixes –**est** and –**ly**.			
I can spell words with the prefixes **dis**– and **un**–.			
I can find out the meaning of a word using a dictionary.			
I can start sentences using an adverb.			
I can organise ideas into a plan before I start writing.			
I can write about a book I like.			
I can use headings, captions, diagrams and tables in a report text.			
Speaking and listening			
I can plan and present my ideas clearly.			

I need more help with ...

_____

_____

_____

_____

_____

What a load of nonsense!

Looks the same, sounds different

 Sort the words from the box into the correct phoneme circle.
An example is given to help you in each circle.

Long ea phoneme

eat

Short ea phoneme

head

snow
dead
now
look
crazy
bread
bloom
bead
neat
yell
gloom
blow
cow
took

ow phoneme

snow

Long ow phoneme

cow

Long oo phoneme

moon

Short oo phoneme

book

Count the syllables

1 Write these words in the correct column.

mother	everyone	could
king	different	eyes
right	animal	laughed
narrator	because	mouse

One syllable	Two syllables	Three syllables	Four syllables

2 Make up some nonsense words with different numbers of syllables.

One syllable	Two syllables	Three syllables	Four syllables

Six slippery silk slippers

 1 Read these tongue twisters.
Try to read each one aloud clearly four times in a row.
Circle the alliteration (words that start with the same phonemes or spelling patterns).

a   The dragon dragged John to join the drumming.

b   Many mini mice make nice
merry music.

c   Peter Piper picked a peck of pickled peppers.

d   Four rivers flowed in the forest.

e   Fish flap fish flip fry.

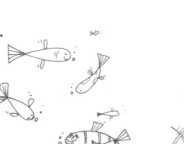

f   Six slippery snakes slipped on silk slippers.

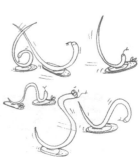

2 Make up silly sentences with these words.

a   dig/did/Dad

_____

b   canaries/can/catch

_____

Acrostics

1 Can you rearrange these lines to make an acrostic about a pet?
(Note: an acrostic is a poem where the first letter of each line
spells a word.)

At night out walking.

Turns up at dinner time.

Curled up in the sun by day.

_____

_____

_____

2 Write an acrostic for TREES and ANIMAL. Use your own words
or words from the box. Add adjectives if you can.

T _____

R _____

E _____

E _____

S _____

tall, thin, reach,
round, rope swing,
red, evergreen,
each, squirrels,
spiders, shade

A _____

N _____

I _____

M _____

A _____

L _____

ant, alligator, newt,
nightingale, insect,
iguana, moth,
moose, mole,
lobster, lion

Shape poem

1 Look at these shape poems.

Twinkle,
twinkle,
little Star.
How I wonder
what you are. Up
above the world so high, like a
diamond in the sky. Twinkle, twinkle, little
Star. How I wonder what you are. Up
above he world so high, like a
diamond in the sky. Twinkle,
twinkle, little Star. How I
wonder what you are. Up
above he world so high,
like a diamond in the sky.
Twinkle,   twinkle,
little   Star.

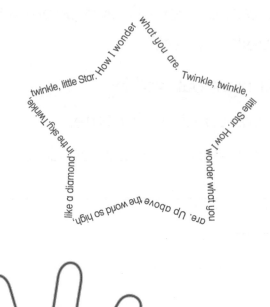

2 Write a shape poem about hands on another piece of paper.

Either:

a Write your words along the outside of a hand shape or

b Completely fill the shape of a hand with your words.

Think of all the things your hands can do. You can use sentences or just words. The words in the box might help you.

> hand, fingers, touch, friends, clap, cook, catch, throw, swim, bat, pat, stroke, rub, type, eat

3 On another piece of paper, draw your own shape poem about a flower or a river.

Mega Wordsearch

 Can you find these high frequency words in the word search?

again	never	through	which
because	new	two	who
find	only	use	why
friends	river	want	work
know	school	wanted	would
live	there	water	
many	thought	where	

a	g	a	i	n	b	c	n	e	w
k	o	b	e	c	a	u	s	e	n
n	l	i	v	e	d	f	i	n	d
o	n	l	y	f	r	r	g	h	t
w	a	n	t	w	h	i	c	h	o
t	h	e	r	e	n	e	v	e	r
g	h	t	w	m	a	n	y	w	i
i	j	w	o	u	l	d	p	h	v
w	h	o	r	s	m	s	q	y	e
k	l	w	k	e	w	a	t	e	r
s	c	h	o	o	l	q	x	z	u
c	k	e	t	h	o	u	g	h	t
t	h	r	o	u	g	h	p	u	k
f	q	e	w	a	n	t	e	d	w

Self-assessment
Unit 9

What a load of nonsense!

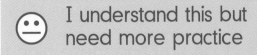
☺ I understand this well

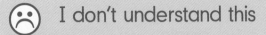
☺ I understand this but need more practice

☹ I don't understand this

Learning Objective	☺	😐	☹
Reading			
I can read words with a long **ar** phoneme.			
I can spot how many syllables are in a word.			
I can spot alliteration in a poem.			
I can answer questions about different types of poem.			
I can use my knowledge of phonemes and spelling patterns to read nonsense words.			
I know the features of an acrostic poem.			
I know the features of a tongue twister.			
I know the features of a shape poem.			
Writing			
I can read and spell all of the high frequency words.			
I can write an acrostic poem.			
I can add adjectives to a shape poem.			
I can use alliteration in a poem.			
Speaking and listening			
I can recite a poem clearly.			

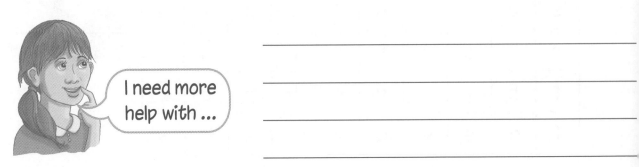

I need more help with ...

_____

_____

_____

_____

The Publishers would like to thank the following for permission to reproduce copyright material:

Acknowledgements

p2, *Monsters* by Philip Waddell from *Read Me Out Loud* chosen by Nick Toczek and Paul Cookson (published by Macmillan); p42 *The End* from *Now We are Six* by AA Milne, text copyright The Trustees of the Pooh Properties 1927, published by Egmont UK Ltd and used with permission; 'The End' by A.A. Milne, from *Now We Are Six* by A.A. Milne, copyright 1927 by E.P. Dutton, renewed © 1955 by A.A. Milne. Used in the United States, Canada and the Philippines by permission of Dutton Children's Books, an imprint of Penguin Young Readers Group, a division of Penguin Random House LLC.

Every effort has been made to trace all copyright holders, but if any have been inadvertently overlooked the Publishers will be pleased to make the necessary arrangements at the first opportunity.

Although every effort has been made to ensure that website addresses are correct at time of going to press, Hodder Education cannot be held responsible for the content of any website mentioned in this book. It is sometimes possible to find a relocated web page by typing in the address of the home page for a website in the URL window of your browser.

Hachette Livre UK's policy is to use papers that are natural, renewable and recyclable products and made from wood grown in well-managed forests and other controlled sources. The logging and manufacturing processes are expected to conform to the environmental regulations of the country of origin.

Orders: please contact Bookpoint Ltd, 130 Milton Park, Abingdon, Oxon OX14 4SB. Telephone: +44 (0)1235 827720. Fax: +44 (0)1235 400454. Lines are open 9.00 a.m.–5.00 p.m., Monday to Saturday, with a 24-hour message answering service. Visit our website at www.hoddereducation.com

© Sarah Snashall 2014
First published in 2014 by
Hodder Education,
An Hachette UK Company
Carmelite House
50 Victoria Embankment
London EC4Y 0DZ

Impression number   13
Year   2020

Cover illustration by Sandy Lightley
Illustrations by Marleen Visser
Typeset in Swissforall 16pt
Printed in Great Britain by Hobbs the Printers, Totton, Hampshire

A catalogue record for this title is available from the British Library

ISBN 978 1471 830242